Hello Kitty

Journal

First published in the UK by
HarperCollins Children's Books in 2009
3 5 7 9 10 8 6 4 2
ISBN 13: 978-0-00-732623-5

Printed and bound in China

Hello Kitty
Journal

HarperCollins *Children's Books*

All About Me...

Stick a photo
of yourself here

Name: _____

Age: _____

Starsign: _____

Address: _____

Home
phone: _____

Mobile
phone: _____

Email: _____

Website: _____

Blog: _____

A Few of my Favourite Things...

My best friend

My favourite colour

My favourite animal

My favourite book

My favourite author

My favourite song

My favourite singer

My favourite band

My favourite instrument

My favourite sport to play

My favourite sport to watch

My favourite treat to eat

My favourite treat to bake

My favourite drink

My favourite place to be

My favourite website

My favourite blog

My favourite television show

My favourite film

Dates to Remember

January

February

March

April

May

my other brothers
birthday

June

end of school

Dates to Remember

July

August

September

October

November

December

Best Friends' Addresses

Keep all your friends' details in one place so you're always ready to write to them!

Name: —————————————
Address: ————————————
—————————————————
Telephone: ————————————
Email: —————————————

Name: —————————————
Address: ————————————
—————————————————
Telephone: ————————————
Email: —————————————

Name: —————————————
Address: ————————————
—————————————————
Telephone: ————————————
Email: —————————————

Name: —————————————
Address: ————————————
—————————————————
Telephone: ————————————
Email: —————————————

Name: —————————————
Address: ————————————
—————————————————
Telephone: ————————————
Email: —————————————

Name: —————————————
Address: ————————————
—————————————————
Telephone: ————————————
Email: —————————————

Name: —————————————
Address: ————————————
—————————————————
Telephone: ————————————
Email: —————————————

Name: —————————————
Address: ————————————
—————————————————
Telephone: ————————————
Email: —————————————

Name: _____   Name: _____
Address: _____   Address: _____
_____   _____

Telephone: _____   Telephone: _____
Email: _____   Email: _____

Name: _____   Name: _____
Address: _____   Address: _____
_____   _____

Telephone: _____   Telephone: _____
Email: _____   Email: _____

Name: _____   Name: _____
Address: _____   Address: _____
_____   _____

Telephone: _____   Telephone: _____
Email: _____   Email: _____

Name: _____   Name: _____
Address: _____   Address: _____
_____   _____

Telephone: _____   Telephone: _____
Email: _____   Email: _____

Name: _____   Name: _____
Address: _____   Address: _____
_____   _____

Telephone: _____   Telephone: _____
Email: _____   Email: _____

Horoscopes

Find out more about you and your friends by studying the signs of the zodiac. Look at the date they were born to see what their star sign says about them.

Aquarius

20th January to 18th February
Element: Air
Personality: Loves the hottest new fashions and is always ready to party!

Pisces

19th February to 20th March
Element: Water
Personality: This sensitive soul is equally happy staying in or going out.

Aries

21st March to 19th April
Element: Fire
Personality: Ready for adventure, Aries is the life and soul of any event.

Taurus

20th April to 20th May
Element: Earth
Personality: You can always rely on a Taurus friend to stay calm and collected.

Gemini

**21st May
to 20th June
Element:** Air
Personality:
Geminis are
interested in
everything and
never stop talking!

Cancer

**21st June to
22nd July
Element:** Water
Personality:
Always kind,
Cancerians are
great for hugs.

Leo

**23rd July
to 22nd August
Element:** Fire
Personality:
Leos make super
faithful friends
and will always
keep your secrets!

Virgo

**23rd August to
22nd September
Element:** Earth
Personality:
For some
practical advice,
Virgos are the
friends to ask.

Libra

**23rd September
to 22nd October
Element:** Air
Personality:
Libra friends are
happy-go-lucky
and can never
make their
minds up!

Scorpio

**23rd October to
21st November
Element:** Water
Personality:
Funny and
clever, Scorpios
are always fun to
be around.

Sagittarius

**22nd November to
21st December
Element:** Fire
Personality:
Multi-talented
Sagittarians
always look on the
bright side of life!

Capricorn

**22nd December to
19th January
Element:** Earth
Personality:
Hard-working and
patient, Capricorns
make very loyal
friends.!

Fun Fashions

If your resolutions involve giving yourself a makeover, why not try fashions from different eras to see which suits you best?

1920s

Flapper girls wore embroidered, beaded shift dresses with drop waists and close-fitting cloche hats. Perfect for a party!

1930s-1940s

Around the time of the Second World War, fashion was all about 'make do and mend'. Clothes were rationed and styles were often quite military.

1950s

The 50s were much more glamorous – lots of dresses with nipped-in waists and full, swinging skirts! It was also when jeans became popular for everyday wear.

1960s

The mini skirt was introduced in the 60s. It was also the time when teenagers chose between being mods or rockers – which style do you prefer?

1970s

Disco time! The 70s is one of my favourite eras, try disco or punk looks, or channel that hippy vibe with tie-dye prints and lots of beads!

1980s

Power dressing and shoulder pads were HUGE in the 80s! So was the New Romantic look, with fab fabrics and lots of ruffles. My favourite 80s look is bright colours, big accessories and even bigger hair!

1990s

The 90s was a mish-mash of styles, with added neon brights.

New Year, New You!

The start of a new year is a great time for new beginnings, whether you want to give yourself or your room a makeover, find a fun hobby or learn something new.

Resolutions

Try and have a mixture of short-term and long-term goals and give yourself plenty of time to achieve them. Don't beat yourself up if you haven't learnt French or how to play the piano by February! Here are some you might like to try:

1. Eat healthy! Aim for five pieces of fruit and veg a day.
2. Play healthy! Try to exercise for at least half an hour each day.
3. Try new styles. If you never wear dresses, but think you'd like to, why not start?
4. Read more. If you don't know where to begin, ask your friends to recommend their favourite books.
5. Explore more. Find out about your local area - I bet there are loads of places to visit that you've never been!
6. Get cooking! I love to try baking new things or experimenting with new cuisines.
7. Get crafty! Why not make all your birthday presents this year instead of buying them? Friends and family will appreciate how personal they are.
8. Learn something new. Whether it is a language, instrument or crafting technique, give yourself plenty of time to really get to grips with it!
9. Make new friends. Join a club or just make an effort with people you don't know at school.
10. Keep a journal! Make sure you fill in what you've been up to every day this year, so you can look back on everything you have done.

January

1

2

3

January

4

5

6

7

8

9

January

10

11

12

13

14

15

January

16

17

18

19

20

21

22

23

24

25

26

27

28

29

30

31

Notes

Valentine's Day

I love to make these gifts to send to my boyfriend, Daniel, but it's just as nice to send Valentine's cards and gifts to friends and family.

Cards

You will need:
* Sheets of card
* Scrap paper
* Scissors
* Sticky tape
* Glue
* Coloured pens or pencils
* Glitter (optional)

Method:
1. Fold a sheet of card in half to make your Valentine's card and decorate the front. You could draw a picture, write a message or cut out heart shapes from the scrap paper and stick them on.
2. Cut out a red or pink heart shape from the scrap paper, and two matching strips of paper, $1/2$ inch wide by approx 7 inches long.
3. Tape the two strips together at one end to make an 'L' shape. Take turns folding each strip of paper across the other, to make a concertina-like spring. Tape the ends together.
4. Stick your heart to one end of the spring, then tape the other end of the spring to the centre of the inside right-hand side of your card. Don't forget to write your message inside, too!
5. Push the spring down and close the card. When you open it, the heart will pop out!

Try this technique with different shapes for Easter, Christmas and birthday cards!

Chocolate fudge

Handmade sweets are the perfect gift, if you can bear to give them away!

Ingredients:
* 1 170g tin evaporated milk
* 450g/16oz granulated sugar
* 1tsp vanilla extract
* 120g/4oz good quality chocolate

Preparation:
1. Grease a square baking tin with butter and put to one side.
2. Ask a grown-up to help you melt the sugar, butter and evaporated milk in a large saucepan over a medium heat and then to bring the mixture to the boil, stirring contantly, for 5-6 minutes.
3. Add the vanilla extract.
4. Ask a grown-up to remove from the heat and add the chocolate until it is melted.
5. Pour the mixture into the baking tin and spread flat with a blunt knife.
6. Leave the fudge to set, transferring it to the fridge when it cools down, for about three hours.
7. Cut into pieces and present to friends wrapped in cellophane and tied with ribbon or in a pretty box.

Why not try adding mini marshmallows, chopped nuts or raisins when you add in the vanilla extract, to make different kinds of fudge?

Photo Memories

A great way to show someone how much you care is by reminding them of the happy times you have shared. Make these gifts and fill them with photos.

Frame

You will need:
* A photo to frame
* 2 sheets of thick card
* Scissors
* Glue
* Pencil
* A sheet of foil, fabric or pretty paper

• Place the photo in the centre of a sheet of card and carefully draw around it. Cut out the shape you have drawn to leave a hole in the card. Cut the outside of the second piece of card to match the first - this will be the back of the frame.

• Take the front of the frame and cover it with your foil, fabric or paper. Glue the photo to the centre of the backing card, then place your frame over it and glue that in place, too.

• To make a stand for your frame, cut a strip from the scrap card you have left over. Make it much wider at one end than the other. Fold the narrow end about 1 inch from the top. Glue the folded end to the back of your frame, so that it can rest on the wider end to stand up.

Album

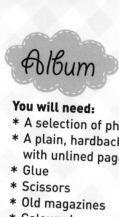

You will need:

* A selection of photos
* A plain, hardback notebook, with unlined pages
* Glue
* Scissors
* Old magazines
* Coloured pens

• Decorate the cover of the notebook with pretty patterns or collage pictures from magazine cuttings.
• Glue photos inside the book, leaving plenty of space at the end to add more in the future.
• You could make decorative borders around each photo, or write captions to remind your friend when they were taken.

February

1

2

3

4

5

6

February

7

8

9

10

11

12

February

13

14

valintines day

15

16

17

18

February

19

20

21

22

23

24

February

25

26

27

28

29 (Leap year only)

Notes

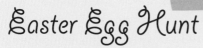

Easter

Easter Egg Hunt

Why not organise an Easter Egg hunt with all your friends?

You will need:
* An egg for each person
* Paints and paintbrushes
* A garden

• Ask a grown-up to hard boil all the eggs and allow them to cool. Everyone should paint their egg with pretty colours and patterns.
• Once the paint has dried, ask a grown-up to hide them around the garden - no peeking!
• Everyone has to search for their own egg. Maybe you could have a chocolate egg as a prize for the first person to find theirs?

Hot Cross Buns

Yummy, I love hot cross buns! They're delicious toasted and buttered!

Ingredients:
* 625g/22oz white or wholemeal flour
* 45g/1.5oz butter
* 45g/1.5oz caster sugar
* 1tsp salt
* 1tsp ground cinnamon
* $1/2$ tsp ground allspice
* $1/2$ tsp grated nutmeg
* $1^{1}/_{2}$ tsp fast-action dried yeast
* 1 egg
* 275ml/9.6fl oz milk
* 100g raisins
* 25g chopped mixed peel
* 125ml/4.4fl oz water

Preparation:

1. Sift 500g/17.5oz of the flour into a large bowl. Rub the butter into the flour with clean hands until you have a mixture that looks like breadcrumbs.
2. Stir in the sugar, salt, cinnamon, allspice, nutmeg and yeast.
3. Break the egg into a separate bowl and beat well.
4. Pour the egg and 275ml/9.6fl oz milk into the dry mixture and stir until it forms a soft dough.
5. Knead the dough on a clean, lightly floured surface for about five minutes. Gradually knead in the raisins and mixed peel.
6. Put the dough back in the bowl and leave in a warm place to rise. This should take about an hour.
7. Knead the dough again on a floured surface to push the air out of it.
8. Divide it into twelve pieces and shape each into a bun.
9. Place the buns on to greased baking trays, making sure there is plenty of space between them, as they will spread during cooking.
10. Ask a grown-up to preheat the oven to 200°C/400°F/gas mark 6.
11. Sift the remaining flour into a bowl and add 125ml/4.4fl oz water. Stir into a smooth paste. Tip the paste into a freezer bag and cut off the corner. Pipe a paste cross on the top of each bun.
12. Bake the buns for fifteen to twenty minutes, or until golden brown. Leave to cool on a wire rack before serving.

Easter Bonnets

Turn any hat into a beautiful Easter bonnet by making these pretty paper flowers and twining them through your hat.

You will need:
* Tissue paper in different colours
* Florist's wire or pipe cleaners
* Scissors
* Glue

For each flower, take three or four sheets of tissue paper and place them on top of each other. Cut out a flower shape, then cut a small hole in the centre of them. Glue a small piece of paper around the end of a piece of wire or pipe cleaner, to make the centre of the flower. Push this through the hole in the paper flowers, and glue them in place. Spread out the petals to make a pretty flower!

March

1

2

3

4

5

6

7

8

9

March

10

11

12

13

14

15

March

16

17

18

19

20

21

March

22

23

24

25

26

27

March

28

29

30

31

Notes

Be a Natural Beauty

There's no need to buy expensive beauty products when you can make your own which are just as good, cheaper and more natural! Why not invite some friends round for a homemade spa day?

Skin Treats

Creamy Honey Mask
This mask is great for all skin types.
Ingredients:
* 1tbsp ground oats
* 1tbsp plain yoghurt
* couple of drops of runny honey
Preparation:
Mix the ingredients together and smooth on to face. Leave for ten minutes then rinse with warm water and pat dry.

Bathing Beauty

Ingredients:
* 1 cup of milk
* 2 tbsp of runny honey
* 1 tbsp sea salt
Preparation:
Add the milk, honey and sea salt to your bath water for super soft and smooth skin.

Spot Saver

Ingredients:
* Toothpaste

Preparation:
Simply dab a little toothpaste on spots to dry them out and lessen redness!

Sweet and Smooth

Exfoliate your skin with this sweet concoction.

Ingredients:
* 2tbsp olive oil
* 1tsp brown sugar

Preparation:
Mix the olive oil and brown sugar to a grainy paste, then massage into your face. Rinse with warm water for super smooth skin.

Hair Help

**Every Kitty loves luscious locks!
Double the recipes for longer hair.**

Deep Clean

To help remove a build-up of hair products, try this rinse. It's great for getting rid of dandruff, too!

Ingredients:
* 2tbsp apple cider vinegar
* 500ml water

Preparation:
Mix the apple cider vinegar with the water. Shampoo hair as normal, then pour the mixture over your hair, avoiding contact with your eyes. Rinse with cold water.

uper Soft

This hair mask will leave you with kitten-soft hair!

Ingredients:
* 1 egg
* 1tbsp olive oil

Preparation:
Mix the egg with olive oil and smooth through hair. If you have time to relax, wrap your hair with cling film or a warm towel and leave the mask for ten minutes before rinsing well with warm water.

Super Shiny

Ingredients:
* Juice of 1 lemon
* Cup of water

Preparation:
Mix the lemon juice and water and use as a rinse after shampooing. Rinse again with the coldest water you can stand - the colder the water, the shinier your hair will be!

Colour Enhancing

Brighten your colour with one of these rinses.

Ingredients:
* Cold coffee for brunettes
* Cold rosehip tea for redheads
* Cold camomile tea with a spoonful of honey for blondes

Preparation:
Pour the cold drink over your hair and leave for five to ten minutes before rinsing.

April

1

2

3

4

5

6

April

7

8

9

10

11

12

13

14

15

16

17

18

19

20

21

22

23

24

25

26

27

28

29

30

Cute Crafts

I love to make things and these crafts all make great gifts!

Friendship Bracelets

Make these bracelets as gifts
for all your friends!

You will need:
* Five 76cm lengths of pretty
  coloured embroidery thread
* Scissors * Sticky tape

Method:
1. Group the threads together and fold them in half, so there is a loop at the top. Tie a knot near the top.
2. Tape the knotted end to a table or flat surface, to stop it moving around while you weave the bracelet.
3. Put each pair of matching coloured threads together and spread them out.
4. Take one of the outer pairs of threads and cross it over the two next to it. Do the same with the outer pair of threads on the opposite side.
5. Keep going in this way, pulling the threads tight as you go.
6. When it is long enough to fit around your wrist, tie all the threads together in a knot. Trim off any excess threads.

This is a very basic plaited design, but there are many others you could experiment with. You could even try adding ribbons or beads into your bracelets!

Perfect Planters

Recycle old yoghurt pots and margarine tubs by turning them into pretty plant pots!

You will need:
* Empty, clean yoghurt or margarine tubs
* Acrylic paints in different colours * Paintbrushes

Method:
Start by choosing a main colour for your plant pot and covering the outside of your tub with it. You might need a couple of coats of paint to cover it fully. Leave it to dry. Now decorate the pot with a pattern of flowers, stripes or polka dots, and leave to dry again.

Why not try planting herbs or cress in your plant pots and keeping them on a kitchen windowsill?

73

Money Box

Encourage your friends to save up
for something special by making
them one of these money boxes!

You will need:
* Empty food containers with lids (cocoa powder and
  gravy cartons are perfect!) * Old newspaper or scrap paper
* Glue * Scissors * Paints * Paintbrushes

Method:

Ask a grown-up to help you cut a slit in the carton, near the top. It
should be big enough to fit a large coin through. Glue newspaper or
scrap paper all over the carton to cover the packaging design and
leave it to dry. Don't forget to leave a space where the slit is! When
the glue is dry, choose a main colour for your money box and paint
the carton. Leave it to dry and then paint any patterns you like on it.
Once all the paint is dry, pop the lid on and it is ready to use!

Memory Board

This is a pretty way to display photos and cards.

You will need:
* A pinboard * Pins * Rolls of coloured ribbons * Scissors

Method:
Pin a length of ribbon tightly from one corner of the board to the corner diagonally opposite, and trim it to size. Repeat pinning lengths of ribbon diagonally across the whole board, each a couple of inches apart. When you have covered the board in one direction, do the same across the opposite diagonal, so that you create a grid of ribbons. Push pins through the ribbons wherever they cross. You can now slot photos, notes and cards through the gaps in the ribbon.

May

1

2

3

4

5

6

May

7

8

9

10

11

12

May

13

14

15

16

17

18

May

19

20

21

22

23

24

May

25

26

27

28

29

30

31

Notes

Home Help

Keeping it Clean

Help your Mama and Papa out around the house with some of these top cleaning tips! They're cheaper and better for the environment than shop-bought cleaning products!

1. Lemons can be the secret cleaning ingredient in any home and they leave everywhere smelling great! Use lemon juice to clean kitchen or bathroom surfaces, or when washing the dishes to make them sparkle.
2. Baking soda has many uses. Sprinkle some on the carpet ten minutes before vacuuming to hide any bad smells, or mix it with water to make a cleaning paste that can be used on almost any surface.
3. White vinegar is brilliant for making mirrors and windows shine! Get an empty spray bottle and fill 1/3 vinegar to 2/3 water. Simply spray and wipe.
4. Olive oil makes a great alternative furniture polish.

Super Storage Solutions

Tidy up your room with some of these great storage ideas.

1. Always keep the boxes when you buy a new pair of shoes. Take a photo of the shoes and stick it to the end of the box. Stack them up inside your wardrobe so you can always find the right pair of shoes for any occasion.

2. Wire racks from the kitchen are perfect for displaying dangly earrings. Prop it up against a wall and hang your earrings on it. No more searching for a matching pair!
3. Colour code your wardrobe to create a rainbow of colour! It'll save you time every morning when deciding what to wear!
4. Go through that pile of magazines on the floor and tear out the pages you want to keep. File them in a ringbinder by subject - recipes, beauty tips and so on. Now recycle the rest!

5. Always searching for your keys? Hang a hook by the door and pop them on there as soon as you get in.
6. Piles of books all over the floor? Ask Mama or Papa to help you put up some shelves to make more space.

7. Pack away winter or summer clothes at the end of each season, to create more room in your wardrobe. Be realistic and don't keep clothes you never wear - why not donate them to charity instead?
8. Add hooks to the inside of your wardrobe door to hang belts, scarves and jewellery on.

Divine Decorations

There are lots of ways to brighten up your bedroom without spending lots of money. Here are a few ideas.

1. Get a coloured bulb for a lamp to create a different atmosphere.
2. Buy frames from charity shops and fill them with your photos or artwork. Framed wallpaper samples can look really cool!
3. A string of fairy lights above the bed or around shelves is always pretty.
4. Keep a vase of fresh flowers in your room - daffodils, carnations or tulips are often cheap and always lovely!
5. Sew beads or lace along the bottom of your curtains for a fresh, new look.
6. Pick a colour scheme and stick with it. Lots of clashing colours make a room look messy, but just a couple of coordinating ones will give your room a really stylish look.

1

2

3

June

4

5

6

7

8

9

June

10

11

12

13

14

15

June

16

17

18

19

20

21

June

22

23

24

25

26

27

28

29

30

Summer Holidays – Going Away

I love holidays, don't you? Whether you're staying at home or travelling somewhere new and exciting, there's always lots to do. Here are some of my tips for having a great time away.

Ready to Go

Use my checklist whenever you are going away to make sure you don't forget anything. Of course, you won't need everything here, but it's a great place to start! I've left some room at the end to include your own essentials.

Essentials
- ○ Passport
- ○ Plane or train tickets
- ○ Travel insurance
- ○ Hotel details
- ○ Guide book
- ○ Local currency
- ○ Teddy
- ○ Friends' addresses for sending postcards

Toiletries
- ○ Toothbrush
- ○ Toothpaste
- ○ Shampoo
- ○ Conditioner
- ○ Shower gel
- ○ Face wash
- ○ Cleanser
- ○ Toner
- ○ Moisturiser
- ○ Cotton wool
- ○ Make-up

Clothes
- ○ Coat or jacket
- ○ Hat
- ○ Scarf
- ○ Gloves
- ○ Jumper
- ○ Cardigan
- ○ T-Shirts
- ○ Tops
- ○ Skirts
- ○ Trousers
- ○ Shorts
- ○ Dresses
- ○ Underwear
- ○ Socks
- ○ Swimsuit
- ○ Pyjamas
- ○ Trainers
- ○ Sandals
- ○ Flip-flops

TELEPHONE

Other Essentials

_____

_____

_____

_____

Hello Kitty Says Hello

It's important to learn about other cultures when you visit them. A great place to start is learning a little of the local language. Here are a few to start you off.

Hello

Ni hao	Chinese
Marhaba	Egyptian
Bonjour	French
Guten Tag	German
Namaste	Indian (Hindi)
Buon giorno	Italian
Kon'nichi wa	Japanese
Jambo	Kenyan (Swahili)
Olá	Portuguese
Hola	Spanish

Goodbye

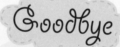

Zai jian	Chinese
Salam	Egyptian
Au revoir	French
Auf Wiedersehen	German
Alavidha	Indian (Hindi)
Ciao	Italian
Say_nara	Japanese
Kwaheri	Kenyan (Swahili)
Adeus	Portuguese
Adios	Spanish

Please

Qing ni	Chinese
Men fadlak	Egyptian
S'il vous plaît	French
Bitte	German
Kripyaa	Indian (Hindi)
Per favour	Italian
Sumimasen	Japanese
Tafadhali	Kenyan (Swahili)
Por favor	Portuguese
Por favor	Spanish

Thank you

Xie xie	Chinese
Shukran	Egyptian
Merci	French
Danke	German
Dhanyavaad	Indian (Hindi)
Grazie	Italian
Arigato	Japanese
Asante sana	Kenyan (Swahili)
Obrigado	Portuguese
Gracias	Spanish

Travel Journal

Why not keep a journal of your travels to help you remember all your adventures?

1. Get a plain notebook and decorate the cover with stickers collected on your trip or cut pictures from old magazines.
2. Stick an envelope inside the cover to store all the ticket stubs from places you visit on your trip.

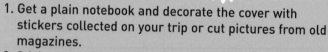

3. Make a list of everything you would like to see and do on your trip, then tick it off as you go. But don't plan too carefully - being spontaneous can lead to all kinds of exciting adventures!
4. Remember to write in the journal every night before bed. Include sights, smells, tastes and feelings so you can relive your holiday once you get home.

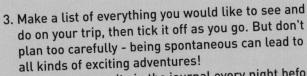

Why not...

Choose a type of souvenir and collect them wherever you go. How about Christmas tree decorations or snow globes?

July

1

2

happy B-Day Wala?
you tried 2

3

4

5

6

July

7

8

9

10

11

12

13

14

15

16

17

18

19

20

21

22

23

24

25

26

27

28

29

30

July

31

Notes

Summer Holidays– Staying Home

I love to travel but a holiday at home can be just as much fun! I bet there are loads of fun things to do in and near your house. Here are my ideas for a summer of fun!

1. Visit a local nature reserve or park and see what animals, birds, insects and plants you can spot.
2. Ask your Mama and Papa if you can invite friends round for a home cinema afternoon. Tell everyone to bring along their favourite DVDs, draw the curtains, and get comfy!
3. Organise a sports day in your garden or a local park. Have different events like running, jumping and throwing. You could even make prizes for your friends to win!
4. Visit the local library and borrow some new books. Try something different to the books you usually read.
5. Get some culture by taking a trip to your local museum or art gallery!
6. Clear out your room and take your old stuff to a charity shop - do you really need that old pair of trainers?
7. Go camping in the garden! Set up a tent in the back garden and invite friends over to camp out. Don't forget to pack for a midnight feast!
8. Use your spare time to learn something new - how about playing the guitar or teaching yourself to knit?

Pretty Postcards

You don't have to go away to send postcards to friends and family - it's always great to receive post! Why not make your own for that personal touch?

You will need:
* Card
* Scissors
* Glue

A selection of the following:
* Coloured pens or pencils
* Pictures cut from old magazines
* Stickers
* Glitter
* Pressed flowers

SAFARI ADVENTURE

HELLO KITTY SAFARI TOURS

To: my
special friend

Hello Kitty

X

Cut your card down to postcard-size and create a collage picture or pattern by arranging cut out pictures, pressed flowers or stickers on one side of the card, then gluing them firmly in place. Ensure the glue is completely dry before turning the card over to write your message. If you're worried about your collage being damaged in the post, you could always pop your postcard in an envelope, which leaves more room on the back for you to write in!

August

1

2

3

4

5

6

7

8

9

10

11

12

13

14

15

16

17

18

19

20

21

22

23

24

25

26

27

28

29

30

31

Notes

Back to School

Ready to Go

Going back to school after the summer holidays is always exciting but it can be daunting. Make sure you're prepared with my tips below.

1. A couple of weeks before you go back, try on your uniform. You might have grown over the holidays and there is no point waiting until the first day back to discover your clothes don't fit you!
2. Make a list of everything you were supposed to have done over the holidays and don't leave it until the night before school starts up again! Reading books and working on projects is always more interesting when you have time to really get into them.
3. Make sure you have everything you're going to need for the upcoming term - I love any excuse to buy new stationery! Decorate your notebooks so they don't get muddled up with everyone else's.
4. Be prepared to make new friends and give everyone a chance - just because you weren't in the same groups last year, doesn't mean you can't be friends this year.

Timetables
Keep track of classes and after-school commitments by making a timetable to stick in your notebook. Follow the template on the opposite page and add in all your own notes.

TIME	MONDAY	TUESDAY	WEDNESDAY	THURSDAY	FRIDAY	SATURDAY	SUNDAY
8am							
9am		Swimming club					
10am						Baking with Mama	
11am							
noon			Reading group				Allotment with Papa
1pm							
2pm							
3pm							
4pm		Guitar lesson		Maths study group	Film club!		
5pm							
6pm							
7pm							
8pm							

Super Study Tips

Staying on top of everything can be tricky, but here are some great ways to get the most out of your study time!

1. Always get plenty of sleep - a tired Kitty is never a witty Kitty!
2. Eat plenty of brain-boosting fish and vegetables.

SCHOOL BUS

3. Have a quiet study area at home and keep it clear of clutter.
4. Plan your studying with my timetable template - you'll never get anything done if you try to do too much at once.

5. Reward your own hard work. If you can get through that difficult science homework, allow yourself a break or a treat before moving on to the next piece of work on your list.

BUS STOP

6. See every day as an opportunity to learn something new and get your friends involved too - why not start a book group or a local history club?
7. Open the dictionary at random and learn a new word each day - see if you can use it in a sentence.
8. Join your local library and get ideas on new books to read from the librarian.

September

1

2

3

4

5

6

September

7

8

9

10

11

12

13

14

15

16

17

18

September

19

20

21

22

23

24

25

26

27

28

29

30

Hallowe'en Hijinks

Hallowe'en is such a fun time of year!

Pumpkin Carving

Trace the image below on to a piece of card, then copy it on to the side of a hollowed-out pumpkin. Ask a grown-up to help you carve the picture to reveal your very own Hello Kitty pumpkin! Carefully place a candle inside and ask the grown-up to light it for you. This makes the perfect decoration for any porch or Hallowe'en party!

Kitty's Fancy Dress

I love any excuse to
dress up, don't you? Here
are some of my favourite
fancy dress looks. I hope they
give you some ideas!

Trick or Treat!

**Make this autumnal treat for any Hallowe'en party
or to hand out to trick or treaters!
It should keep well for up to a week.**

Parkin

Ingredients:
* 100g/3.5oz black treacle
* 75g/2.6oz golden syrup
* 150g/5.3oz butter
* 175g/6.2oz plain flour
* 275g/9.7oz oatmeal
* 2tsp ground ginger
* 1tsp ground cinnamon
* Pinch grated nutmeg
* 1tsp bicarbonate of soda
* 150ml/5.3 fl oz full fat milk

Preparation:
1. Ask a grown-up to pre-heat the oven to 180°C/350°F/gas mark 4.
2. Ask them to help you melt the treacle, golden syrup, butter and sugar in a pan over a low heat. Leave it to one side to cool.
3. Sift the flour and spices into a bowl and stir in the oatmeal.
4. Beat the egg and milk in another bowl with a fork, then add the bicarbonate of soda.
5. Stir the milk and egg mixture into the flour, then add the butter and treacle mixture. Gently mix everything together.
6. Line a square cake tin with greaseproof paper and pour in the mixture.
7. Bake for 50 minutes to an hour, until the cake is firm to the touch.
8. Leave to cool before cutting into squares to eat!

October

1

2

3

October

4

5

6

7

8 happy B-Day TOBY your traning 11

9

10

11

12

13

14

15

16

17

18

19

20

21

October

22

23

24

25

26

27

28

29

30

31

Notes

Slumber Party

Check out my top tips for a fab slumber party!

1. Always check with Mama and Papa before inviting anyone over. See if they have any rules they want you to stick to and make sure everyone knows what they are.

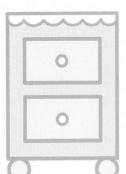

2. Make sure you will have enough places for all your guests to sleep. Ask them to bring extra sleeping bags or pillows if you don't have enough.
3. Have plenty planned to keep everyone entertained. Maybe set up a home cinema with some popcorn and favourite DVDs, or organise some party games like pass the parcel or truth or dare!
4. Whip up some beauty treats (see pages 62-65) and turn your sleepover into a spa! Why not ask everyone to bring a different nail varnish and give each other manicures?

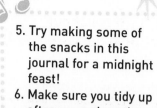

5. Try making some of the snacks in this journal for a midnight feast!

6. Make sure you tidy up after yourselves the next day. If Mama and Papa are happy with how the party went, they're much more likely to let you do it again!

Slumber Party Checklist for Guests:
- ⭘ Pyjamas
- ⭘ Toothbrush
- ⭘ Favourite teddy
- ⭘ Extra bedding

Midnight Snacks

There are lots of sweet treats to try throughout this journal, but why not balance them out with some of these healthy dips?

Chop up lots of fresh vegetables into strips - try carrots, celery, cucumber and peppers - and arrange them on plates around bowls of dip.

Hummus

Ingredients:
* 200g/7oz tinned chickpeas
* 2tbsp tahini
* 2 cloves of garlic
* Juice of 1/2 lemon
* Pinch of salt
* Olive oil
* Paprika

Preparation:
Drain and rinse the chickpeas, then ask a grown-up to whizz them to a smooth paste in a food processor. Peel and crush the garlic cloves and add them, the lemon juice, salt and tahini to the mixture and whizz again. Taste and add more tahini or lemon juice as required. Serve the hummus in a bowl with a drizzle of olive oil and sprinkle of paprika on top.

Salsa

Ingredients:
* 3 tomatoes, roughly chopped
* 1 small onion, roughly chopped
* Handful of coriander, roughly chopped
* 1tbsp lemon juice
* 2tbsp tomato puree
* 1/2 tsp sugar
* Salt and pepper to season

Preparation:
Mix all the ingredients together in a bowl and serve!

Guacamole

Ingredients:
* 2 ripe avocados
* 1 tomato, finely chopped
* 2 cloves of garlic, crushed
* 1tbsp lemon juice
* Handful of coriander, roughly chopped
* Salt to season

Preparation:
Cut the avocados in half, remove the stones and scoop out the flesh. Mash it in a bowl with the other ingredients and serve!

Cucumber and Mint Dip

Ingredients:
* 6tbsp natural yoghurt
* 1/2 cucumber, diced
* Handful of fresh mint, finely chopped.

Preparation:
Simply mix all the ingredients together and serve with an extra sprig of mint on the top!

1

2

3

4

5

6

7

8

9

10

11

12

November

13

14

15

16

17

18

19

20

21

22

23

24

25

26

27

28

29

30

Kitty Loves Christmas

Great Gifts

Christmas is my favourite time of year! I love buying presents, decorating the tree and cooking up Christmas goodies. Here are some ideas for fun, inexpensive gifts for your friends and family.

Mama - One of the best things you can give your Mama is time to relax! Make her a promise to help out with the chores every week for the next year and stick to it! Why not mix her up one of the beauty treats you discovered back in April, put it in a clean jar and tie a ribbon around it? Make sure she uses it quickly, as natural treats don't last long!

Papa - Papas need help round the house, too! Why not offer to organise the garage or the shed (Mama will love this, too!)? Sort tiny things like nails and screws into jars and brush away all those spiders! Maybe you could make Papa a frame from page 34, with a picture of you and him together in it?

Sister - Encourage your sister to love cooking as much as you do, by making her a special recipe book! Buy a nice notebook and decorate the cover with pictures of tasty treats, then write all your favourite recipes inside. If you're lucky, maybe she'll bake you something sweet to say thank you!

Brother - How about making your brother a film or music journal? Again, buy a nice notebook and decorate the cover with pictures of his favourite films or bands. Start him off by listing some must-see films or must-hear music inside. Now he has plenty of space to write his reviews!

Friends - How about trying some of my cute craft ideas from May? Or baking some delicious cookies and wrapping them up in cellophane with a ribbon bow? You could even get them their own journal for next year, so they can be as inspired as you!

Cracking Christmas

Make Christmas crackers with little gifts in for your Christmas dinner table.

You will need:
* Cardboard tubes – one for each cracker
* Small gifts – one for each cracker
* Coloured tissue paper
* Sticky tape
* Ribbon or thread
* Glitter or foil
* Glue
* Cracker snaps (optional, available from craft shops)
* Paper, cut into small strips
* Coloured pens

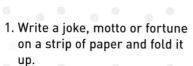

1. Write a joke, motto or fortune on a strip of paper and fold it up.
2. Place the folded paper, snap and gift inside the cardboard tube, so the ends of the snap stick out of each end. You may need to cut the tube to be slightly shorter.
3. Roll a sheet of tissue paper around the tube and hold it in place with sticky tape.
4. Tie a piece of ribbon or thread around the tissue paper at either end of the tube, to create the cracker shape. Make sure the snap is sticking out of both ends of the tube.
5. Trim any excess paper from the ends of the cracker, or cut zigzag patterns at the edges.
6. Decorate the cracker with glitter or foil patterns. If your cracker is for a particular person, write their name on the side and use it to show where they should sit at the dinner table.

Ready for Next Year!

If you're clever, Christmas is the perfect time to prepare for the following Christmas! Try these tips for saving time, money and the environment.

1. Recycle this year's Christmas cards by turning them into next year's gift tags! Cut out any cute pictures and keep them in a box, ready to add a loop of ribbon and your festive message to them next Christmas.
2. If you're careful when you unwrap your presents, you can keep any undamaged wrapping paper and use it to wrap your presents next year.
3. Check out the sales and buy all your cards, wrappings and decorations half price, then put them away for next year.

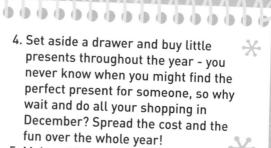

4. Set aside a drawer and buy little presents throughout the year - you never know when you might find the perfect present for someone, so why wait and do all your shopping in December? Spread the cost and the fun over the whole year!
5. Make a Christmas book. Cut out articles and recipes from magazines and store them all together to give you lots of festive ideas.
6. Make a list of everyone who sent you a Christmas card or message, so you remember to send them one next year.

December

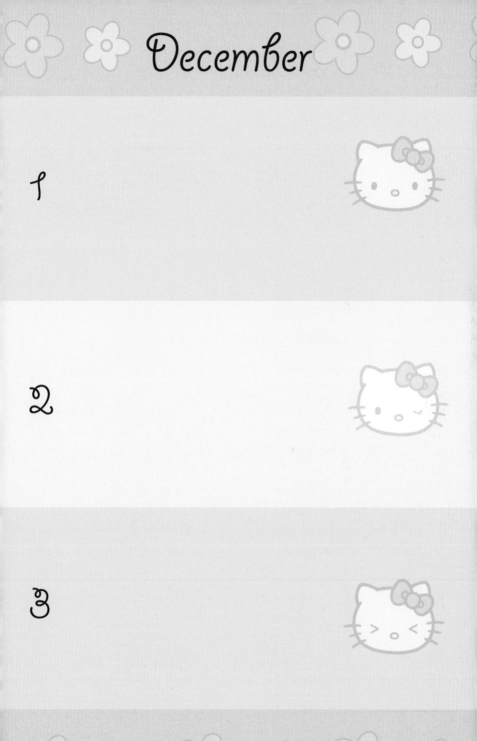

1

2

3

December

4

5

6

7

8

9

December

10

11

12

13

14

15

December

16

17

18

19

20

21

December

22

23

24

25

26

27

December

28

29

30

31

Notes